CONTENTS

GROOVY GAMES!

FREAK I.D.!

Crooks are trying to pose as members of
the Mystery gang using fake I.D. cards!
Can you find one thing wrong with each?

Real I.D.

Member of Mystery Inc.

20373   scooby-dee

Fake I.D.s

A Member of Mystery Stink.

20373   scooby-dee

B Member of Mystery Inc.

203373   scooby-dee

C Member of Mystery Inc.

20373   scooby-dee

D Member of Mystery Inc.

20373   scooby-dee

E Member of Mystery Inc.

20373   sDooby-dee

PHOTO FIX!

Scooby was so hungry, he tried to eat the team photo!
Can you help fix it by spotting the only
piece that doesn't belong?

SCOOBY WHO?

Find out who is hiding in these lines by shading each shape with a dot inside!

8

THOSE MEDDLING KIDS

WRITER - JOHN ROZUM
PENCILLER - SCOTT GROSS
INKER - JORGE PACHECO
LETTERER - TRAVIS LANHAM
COLORIST - HEROIC AGE
EDITOR - NACHIE CASTRO

DEEP BENEATH THE WAVES IN THE REGION KNOWN AS "THE GRAVEYARD OF SHIPS"...

THAT'S THE LAST OF THEM.

THIS GLOWING SEAWEED SURE IS A NUISANCE.

THE GLOWING STUFF RUBS OFF ONTO WHATEVER IT TOUCHES.

10

13

NOW I JUST HAVE TO SUBMERGE AND TOW IT BACK IN THROUGH THE HIDDEN ENTRANCE TO MY UNDERWATER CAVE, AND I CAN CALL IT A NIGHT.

CLINK

16

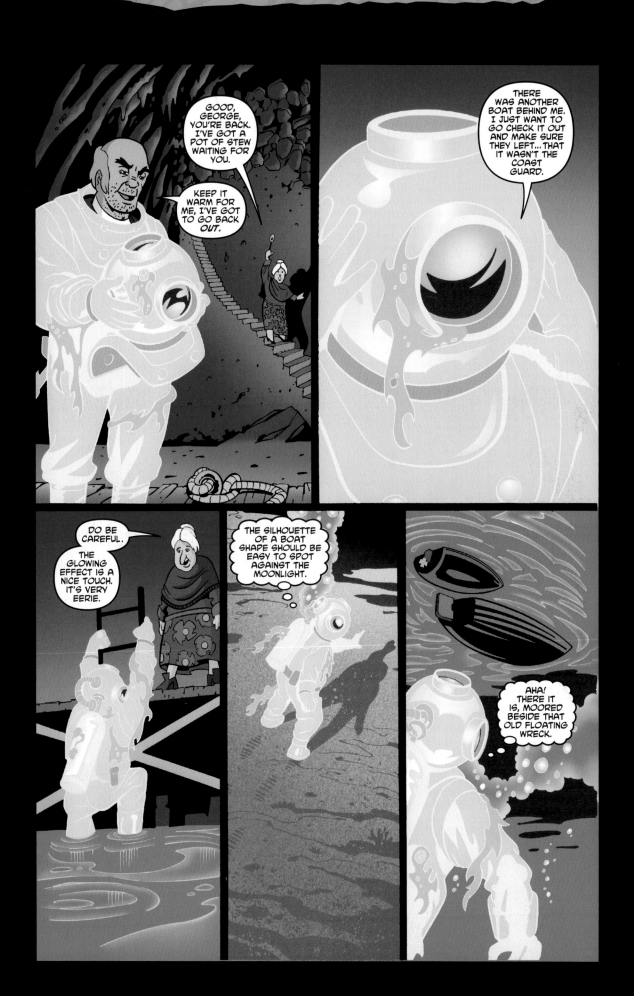

18

SCUBA-DOO!

Can you help Scooby get through the slippery seaweed maze without meeting any demonic divers?

Brain Rating
Easy

Start

Finish

23

Inside... THE MYSTERY MACHINE

Ever wondered how the Mystery Machine works? This top-secret fact-file gives you the guided tour!

SPOOK TRACKER

This high tech radar gives the gang the location of any nearby monsters!

Binoculars

Shaggy & Scoob's snack fridge

Daphne's sunglasses selection

Emergency water supply

Daphne's make-up bag

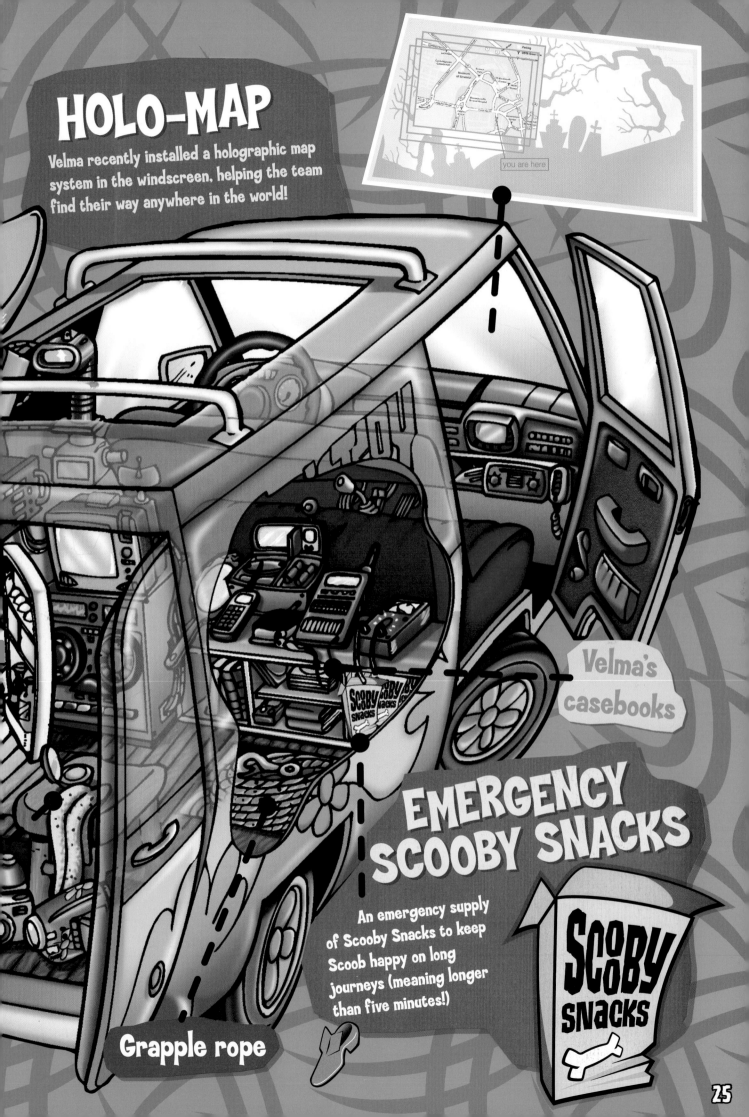

HOLO-MAP

Velma recently installed a holographic map system in the windscreen, helping the team find their way anywhere in the world!

you are here

Velma's casebooks

EMERGENCY SCOOBY SNACKS

An emergency supply of Scooby Snacks to keep Scoob happy on long journeys (meaning longer than five minutes!)

Grapple rope

SCOOBY SNACKS

Haunted Mansion!

Take the large cardboard box and cut two card rectangles to fit inside it. Tape them into place - these will make the floors.

Cut a rectangle of card so that it can slot inside the top floor and create two rooms. Before you fix it in place, cut a rectangle out of the card to make a doorway. Now tape the wall into place.

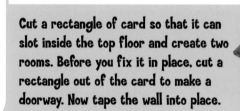

Glue a large card rectangle to the bottom of the box. Use this as a base for attaching lots of balls of rolled up newspaper. These will become rocks and the bottom floor of the house will be a spooky underground cellar! Make a secret tunnel by sticking half of a cardboard tube to the base, and build the newspaper up around it.

YOU WILL NEED:

A large cardboard box, thick card, cardboard tubes, small cardboard boxes, newspaper, glue, scissors, paints and paintbrush

4 To make the roof, cut two cardboard rectangles to size and tape them into place at an angle. Cut two cardboard triangles to fill in each end of the roof. Cut a toothpaste box in half to make two chimneys. Cut another small box in half to make two dormer windows and tape into place.

5 Create a doorway on the side of the house by cutting a cardboard tube in half. Draw a rectangle on the house as a door frame and tape the cardboard tubes in place on either side. Finish with a card rectangle taped on top of the tubes as a canopy.

6 Now you are ready to paint your house in spooky Scooby colours. Paint the rocks grey, the walls purple and the roof blue. Add some yellow to light up the windows.

HERE'S WHAT THE BACK LOOKS LIKE...

Now turn the page to find out how to make some extra-spooky touches for your house!

27

Haunted Mansion Continued!

Now you have created your haunted mansion, you need to add some really spooky touches! Here are some handy hints on how to decorate your house.

Room with a view!

Add some balconies to the side of your house. Cut a door shape into the outside wall. Cut a rectangle of card and fold three of the sides in to make a narrow box shape. Tape the three sides into position at the bottom of the window to create a balcony for your action figures to stand on!

Trap door terror!

Create a terrifying trap door leading to the cellar. Use a pencil to draw some floorboards on the floor. Then draw a square in the middle of the floor and cut out three sides of it. You can even write 'Thud!' on the floor below to show where your victims will land!

Freaky Furniture!

Decorate the interior of the house with some crazy furniture. Use small cardboard boxes to make wardrobes, chests and old trunks. Paint them brown and add details in black. Draw some spooky eyes and ghoulish hands on paper, colour them in, cut them out and stick them to the furniture to add some Scooby scariness!

Weird Windows!

Draw some rectangles on the back of the house and paint them yellow to give them a ghostly glow. Add the shadows of some ghoulish spooks in orange. Outline the windows in black.

THE MONSTER FILES

VELMA'S MONSTERS OF THE WORLD: WEREWOLVES

JOHN ROZUM: STORY
DAN DAVIS: ART
HEROIC AGE: COLORS
MIKE SELLERS: LETTERS
JEANINE SCHAEFER: EDITOR

HELLO, EVERYONE. THANKS FOR JOINING ME.

TODAY WE ARE GOING TO BE TALKING ABOUT WEREWOLVES!

WEREWOLVES

"THE WORD "WEREWOLF" ACTUALLY MEANS "MAN-WOLF," A PERSON WHO UNDER CERTAIN CONDITIONS CAN TRANSFORM HIMSELF INTO A WOLF.

"THIS IS A VERY OLD BELIEF THAT BELONGS TO DIFFERENT CULTURES ALL OVER THE WORLD."

"WOLVES AREN'T THE ONLY ANIMALS THAT PEOPLE WERE BELIEVED TO CHANGE INTO. NEW GUINEA HAD WERE-CROCODILES, EUROPE HAD WERE-BEARS, INDIA HAD WERE-TIGERS, AND AFRICA HAD LEOPARD-MEN AND HYENA-MEN."

SO, HOW DOES A PERSON TRANSFORM INTO AN ANIMAL? WELL, GODS COULD DO IT AT WILL, BUT FOR NORMAL, MORTAL PEOPLE, THERE WERE A NUMBER OF WAYS.

IN SOME CASES, A PERSON WOULD BREAK A SACRED LAW, AND BE TURNED INTO A WOLF AS PUNISHMENT. CURSES COULD TURN INNOCENT PEOPLE OR CRIMINALS INTO WOLVES, USUALLY FOR PERIODS OF SEVERAL YEARS.

"ACCORDING TO GREEK MYTH, KING LYCAEON ANGERED THE GOD ZEUS, AND WAS TRANSFORMED INTO A WOLF AS PUNISHMENT.

"THIS GAVE US THE WORD 'LYCANTHROPE,' THE TECHNICAL TERM FOR A WEREWOLF.

"ACCORDING TO SOME, SLEEPING OUTDOORS UNDER A FULL MOON ON A FRIDAY NIGHT WILL DO IT. FULL MOONS ARE OFTEN ASSOCIATED WITH WEREWOLVES, BUT MOSTLY IN THE MOVIES.

"OTHERS SAY THAT DRINKING WATER FROM A WOLF'S FOOTPRINT OR FROM A STREAM WHERE A WOLF PACK HAS DRUNK WILL CAUSE THE PERSON TO CHANGE.

"PEOPLE WITH CONNECTING EYEBROWS, POINTY EARS AND RING FINGERS AS LONG AS THEIR MIDDLE FINGERS WERE THOUGHT TO BE WEREWOLVES.

SOMETIMES, IT WAS SIMPLY BECAUSE YOUR ANCESTORS COULD DO IT, BUT THE MOST COMMON METHOD OF TRANSFORMATION WAS EITHER THROUGH MAGIC CHARMS, SALVES, SPELLS, AND RITUALS, OR...

"DURING THE RENAISSANCE, TRANSFORMATION BECAME ASSOCIATED WITH WITCHES WHO WERE BELIEVED TO BE ABLE TO TURN INTO CATS, HARES, AND TOADS."

"..BY PUTTING ON THE SKIN OF A WOLF, OR A WOLF MASK, AND BEHAVING LIKE THE ANIMAL.

"SOMETIMES ALL IT TAKES IS A BELT MADE FROM THE SKIN OF THAT ANIMAL.

"UNLIKE WHAT YOU SEE IN THE MOVIES, IT WAS RARE FOR WEREWOLVES OF LEGEND TO BE AT ALL MAN-LIKE IN APPEARANCE.

"IN THE MIDDLE AGES, AN EXCESSIVELY HAIRY MAN CLAIMING TO BE A WEREWOLF WOULD BE VIEWED AS BEING A BIT OF A NUT."

 DO YOU *WANT* TO *SEE* A MAN TURN INTO A *WOLF?* JUST *REARRANGE* THE PANELS BELOW INTO THE *CORRECT ORDER.*

MOST LEGENDS *AGREE* THAT THE WOLF *AUTOMATICALLY* TURNS BACK INTO A PERSON DURING THE *DAY,* OR WHEN THEY ARE KILLED.

SOMETIMES *MAGIC* IS NECESSARY, BUT OFTEN YOU CAN *STOP* A WEREWOLF WITH ORDINARY *WEAPONS,* SILVER BULLETS ARE THE INVENTION OF THE MOVIES. SOMETIMES, ALL YOU *NEED* TO DO IS CALL OUT THEIR HUMAN *NAME,* AND THEY'LL TURN BACK INTO A PERSON.

BUT, *I FIND* THAT THE *BEST* WAY TO TURN A WEREWOLF BACK INTO A MAN IS SIMPLY TO PULL OFF HIS *MASK.*

GRMBLE MUTTER GRMP.

THE END

IN THE FRAME!

Liven up your computer monitor with this spooky-doo computer frame! Like, beware of those giant spiders!

YOU WILL NEED:

Thick card, paints and a paintbrush, scissors, a bowl of PVA glue mixed with water, a ruler, newspaper, wool, kitchen paper, googly eyes, sticky fixers.

1

Measure your computer screen. Draw a rectangle on a piece of thick card, the same size as your screen. Measure carefully and draw a border 7cms thick around this. Cut out the frame.

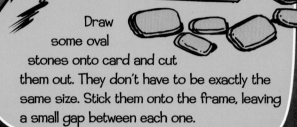

2

Draw some oval stones onto card and cut them out. They don't have to be exactly the same size. Stick them onto the frame, leaving a small gap between each one.

3

Draw some spider shapes on card and cut them out. Stick them onto the frame. Keep one spider spare, to hang from the bottom of the frame.

4

Pad the spiders' bodies out with scrunched-up kitchen paper and then cover the whole frame with a layer of kitchen paper and PVA glue. Make sure you push your brush into all the nooks and crannies! The kitchen paper should create a bumpy, textured effect on the stones.

5

Cut some lengths of wool. Dip them in PVA glue and arrange them in the corners of the frame in a cobweb pattern. Let one length of wool hang down from the bottom corner and stick your spare spider onto it. Leave to dry.

6

Paint the frame with grey paint and add details with black and white. Mix some of the grey with the black paint to make a darker shade, perfect for adding some shade and texture to the stones. Glue googly eyes onto the spiders. Once it is dry, use sticky fixers to fix your frame onto your computer monitor.

HOW TO DRAW FrEd

He's the quick-thinking leader of the Mystery, Inc. gang. Draw your own portrait of Freddy!

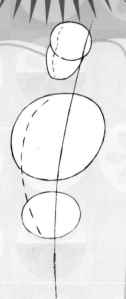

Start by drawing three circles for his head, body and hips. Add an oval for his chin. Draw a line to plot out the position of his legs and feet.

Now add his neck and shoulders. Draw sausage shapes for his arms. Add two long lines for his legs and sketch in his feet.

Add Fred's hair and his trademark Ascot tie! Draw lines for his fingers and the details on his shoes.

Finally, add the details to his face. Rub out any unwanted lines, use a black pen to draw over your finished outline and colour him in!

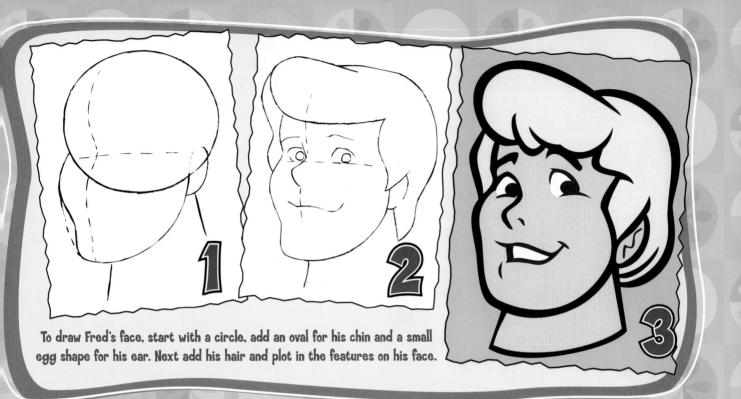

To draw Fred's face, start with a circle, add an oval for his chin and a small egg shape for his ear. Next add his hair and plot in the features on his face.

Now try it for yourself...

HIGH UP ON THE WORLD'S TALLEST MOUNTAIN – *MOUNT EVEREST* – TWO CLIMBERS, PROFESSOR ROBINSON JEFFRIES AND HIS NEPALESE MOUNTAIN GUIDE, PEMBA SHERPA, HAVE MADE AN *AMAZING DISCOVERY...*

SEE, PROFESSOR JEFFRIES, AS I PROMISED YOU -- WE HAVE FOUND IT!

SO, DO NOT *DRAG ME TO MY DEATH...* THIS *ANCIENT STONE* WILL WAIT.

AND THANKS TO *YOU...* AND *MY MANUSCRIPT...THE LOST KINGDOM OF SHANGRI-LA* AWAITS!

HA-HA-HA -- YES, PEMBA, YOU *FOUND IT!* WITHOUT A DOUBT, THE BEST GUIDE IN ALL THE HIMALAYAS. THAT'S WHY I *HIRED YOU!*

NO...YOU VOWED THIS WOULD BE AS FAR AS WE WOULD GO! IN FACT, EVEN THIS SPOT WHERE WE NOW STAND IS *FORBIDDEN!*

FORBIDDEN?! WHO FORBIDS IT, PEMBA?! YOU?

HIM!

DO YOU NOT *HEAR?!* HE *COMES!* SO... WE GO!

CAN'T QUIT...WE'RE *TOO CLOSE*...I'LL CONTINUE ON TO SHANGRI-LA ...

...ALONE!

NO, PROFESSOR! THE LINE...SNAPPED!

IIIEEEEE!!! THE LEGEND...

THE YETI!

RROOAAARR

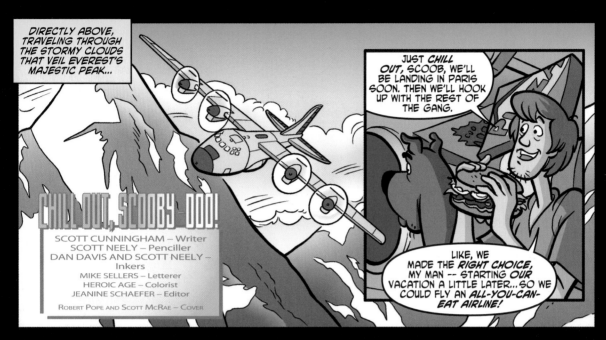

DIRECTLY ABOVE, TRAVELING THROUGH THE STORMY CLOUDS THAT VEIL EVEREST'S MAJESTIC PEAK...

CHILL OUT, SCOOBY-DOO!

SCOTT CUNNINGHAM – Writer
SCOTT NEELY – Penciller
DAN DAVIS AND SCOTT NEELY – Inkers
MIKE SELLERS – Letterer
HEROIC AGE – Colorist
JEANINE SCHAEFER – Editor

Robert Pope and Scott McRae – Cover

JUST *CHILL OUT*, SCOOB, WE'LL BE LANDING IN PARIS SOON. THEN WE'LL HOOK UP WITH THE REST OF THE GANG.

LIKE, WE MADE THE *RIGHT CHOICE*, MY MAN -- STARTING *OUR* VACATION A LITTLE LATER...SO WE COULD FLY AN *ALL-YOU-CAN-EAT* AIRLINE!

REAH -- *RALL-ROU-RAN-REAT!*

I, ALPHONSE LAFLEUR, ZEE WORLD-FAMOUS *MONSTER HUNTER*-- UH, I MEAN, ZEE WORLD-FAMOUS HOST OF *LE MONDE GRANDE TOURS*, HAVE AN *IMPORTANT ANNOUNCEMENT* TO MAKE.

OUR *ALL-YOU-CAN-EAT* AIRLINE HAS BEEN *TEMPORARILY SUSPENDED*...SINCE ZEE TWO OF YOU HAVE *EATEN ALMOST EVERYTHING!*

WELL, I'VE GOT AN ANNOUNCEMENT *TOO!* I HAVE A *CELL PHONE* AND I'M *NOT* AFRAID TO *USE IT*...TO CALL THE PROPER U.S. GOVERNMENT AGENCY IN CHARGE OF *ALL-YOU-CAN-EAT!*

LIKE, HELLLLP!!!

GUYS? ARE YOU *OK*? WHAT'S *HAPPENING*? *WHERE ARE YOU*?!

AS IF THINGS WEREN'T BAD ENOUGH, NOW MY EARS ARE RINGING!

RINNGG

LIKE, UNLESS IT'S *FREEZING* IN PARIS, FRED, OUR FLIGHT WAS *MAJORLY* RE-ROUTED. AND NOW ≈GULP≈ I THINK SCOOB AND I ARE ABOUT TO GO FROM FREQUENT FLIERS...TO FREQUENT *CRIERS*!

HELPPP--

RELPPP--

THEY'RE *BREAKING UP*.

MAYBE *LITERALLY*!

FREDDY LOSES THE CONNECTION -- BUT NOT SHAG AND SCOOB'S LAST *LOCATION*, THANKS TO THE BUILT-IN GLOBAL POSITIONING SATELLITE SYSTEM ON HIS HIGH-TECH CELL PHONE. IT TRACKS SHAG AND SCOOB'S FINAL ≈GULP≈ POSITION AS *MT. EVEREST*, AND THE GANG QUICKLY LEAVE PARIS BEHIND...FOR A *CHILLIER CLIME*.

IT IS *MY FAULT*! I HAVE ANGERED THE *YETI*, BY TAKING A FOREIGNER INTO THE *FORBIDDEN LANDS*.

MEANWHILE, BACK IN THE HIMALAYAS, A SUDDEN STORM DRIVES PROFESSOR JEFFRIES AND PEMBA BACK TO THE GUIDE'S VILLAGE. PEMBA WASTES NO TIME SPREADING WORD OF HIS *YETI* SIGHTING, WHICH PROMPTS A MASS *EVACUATION*. THEN PEMBA VISITS THE VILLAGE'S MONASTERY TO PERFORM A *SPECIAL RITUAL*...

MINGA, MY *SISTER*, WHAT ARE YOU DOING HERE? YOU SHOULD BE *LEAVING* THIS PLACE WITH *THE OTHERS*!

I'M BRINGING YOU SOME *HOT TEA*! THAT'S WHAT I AM DOING!

HOT TEA? NO...YOU MUST *LISTEN TO ME*...

NOW TAKE OFF THOSE *SILLY HEADPHONES* AND DO AS YOU ARE *TOLD*! THE *CREATURE* IS ANGERED AND IT IS NO *LONGER SAFE*!

I'M NOT A *LITTLE GIRL*, ANYMORE, PEMBA! STOP TRYING TO *FRIGHTEN ME* WITH YOUR *MONSTER STORIES*!

SO, MINGA... YOU DON'T BELIEVE IN THE ABOMINABLE SNOWMAN?

WHEN I WAS YOUNG, MY BROTHER TOLD ME SCARY STORIES: *"THE YETI IS GOING TO GET YOU!"* NOW HE TELLS THE STORIES TO *EVERYONE*...

THE YETI IS REAL...AND *DANGEROUS!* THAT IS WHY I AM BURNING THE *SACRED JUNIPER BRANCH*, WHY I AM OFFERING PRAYERS TO THE GREAT MOUNTAIN. PERHAPS *SHE* WILL LOOK KINDLY UPON US, AND SEND US SOME SIGN OF *GOOD FORTUNE*...

W-W-WE'RE S-S-SURE *L-L-LUCKY* M-M-MY P-P-PARACHUTE S-S-STOPPED T-T-TEARING.

RIPP

SLAP

R-R-REAH... R-R-RUCKY.

YAAAAAAA

RAAAAAAA

CRASH

WHOA...WE... WE *MADE* IT, SCOOB. WONDER WHAT BROKE OUR FALL?

REAH... RONDER?

M-M-MONSTER! YAAAAAAA!!!

RAAAAAA!!!

DRAWN BY THE SOUND OF THE FIRST CRASH, PEMBA, MINGA AND JEFFRIES ARRIVE IN TIME TO WITNESS THE SECOND!

RUN FOR YOUR LIVES!

CRASH

REAH - RRRRUN!

AHHHH, WELCOME, MOST HONORED GUESTS, TO THE RANGPOCHE MONASTERY. DO NOT BE AFRAID.

I SEE YOU HAVE DISCOVERED OUR HIDDEN CHAMBER!

MAN, WE ALSO DISCOVERED HOW THIN YOUR WALLS ARE!

RAND A RONSTER!

THE HIGH LAMA LEADS THE GROUP BACK INTO THE SECRET CHAMBER OF THE YETI...

SEE, MY FRIENDS, THE CREATURE YOU FEAR IS NO CREATURE AT ALL, BUT SIMPLY OUR ALTARPIECE. IN THIS CHAMBER, WE OFFER SACRIFICE TO THE YETI -- THE HALF MAN, HALF ANIMAL WHO LIVES IN THE SNOW CAVES, HIGH ON THE MOUNTAIN.

SEE, SCOOB, RELAX. IT'S JUST A CREEPY CARVING.

RULP!

BUT YOU ARE SAFE HERE, UNDER THE POWER OF THE CRYSTAL.

FANTASTIC! AMAZING! MAY I EXAMINE IT...CLOSER?

YOU MAY NOT! THE CRYSTAL IS SACRED! ITS MYSTICAL GLOW PROTECTS US FROM THE CREATURE.

HA-HA! BEFORE I AM THROUGH, IT'S ZEE CREATURE THAT WILL NEED ZEE PROTECTING FROM ME!

CHECK IT OUT, SCOOB, IT'S OUR BOGUS TOUR GUIDE! HEY DUDE, YOUR EXIT POLICY COULD USE SOME WORK!

MY SINCEREST APOLOGIES! YOU SEE, THERE WAS A TERRIBLE MISHAP! I WAS SO WORRIED FOR YOU THAT I JUMPED FROM ZEE PLANE MYSELF, DESPERATE TO SAVE YOU!

DESPERATE, TOO, WAS I, TO SAVE YOUR SCOOBY SNACKS!

MUNCH-MUNCH- THANKS, MAN. ALL'S FORGIVEN!

MUNCH-MUNCH- ROR-RIVEN.

MUNCH-MUNCH-KNOW WHO ELSE MUST BE DESPERATE TO SAVE US, SCOOB? THE REST OF THE GANG! BUT THE CELL'S DEAD.

YOU CAN CALL YOUR FRIENDS FROM THE WEATHER STATION. I'LL TAKE YOU THERE.

NO! THE ONLY PLACE YOU ARE GOING IS DOWN THE MOUNTAIN -- AWAY FROM DANGER!

RANGER?!

YES, RANGER! UH, *DANGER!* BECAUSE THE FARTHER UP THE MOUNTAIN YOU GO, THE CLOSER TO *THE YETI'S CAVE* YOU GET!

YOU DIDN'T HAVE TO COME, PROFESSOR JEFFRIES!

NONSENSE! SAFETY IN NUMBERS, YOU KNOW!

MEANWHILE, SOMEWHERE IN THE *BLAZING SUDAN DESERT,* THE GANG STRUGGLE TO MAKE THEIR WAY TO THOSE *CHILLY CLIMES* MENTIONED EARLIER.

I JUST FINISHED TRANSLATING THIS ARTICLE FROM THE LOCAL PAPER, AND GET THIS, THERE'S BEEN A RASH OF *YETI SIGHTINGS* OUT WHERE SHAG AND SCOOB HAVE DISAPPEARED!

YOU KNOW HOW THEY GET ANYWHERE NEAR *MYSTERIOUS CREATURES...*BETTER STEP ON IT!

WE'D BE THERE BY NOW, IF IT WASN'T FOR FREDDY'S *SHORTCUT!*

HEY, DAPH, I GOT US BACK ON TRACK, DIDN'T I?"

YEAH, FREDDY, BUT ONLY AFTER MAKING ME TALK TO THE CAMEL VENDOR. WHAT IS IT WITH MEN AND ASKING FOR DIRECTIONS ANYWAY?

SHAGGY AND SCOOBY QUICKLY CHOW THROUGH THE SUPPLY OF SCOOBY SNACKS (MOUNTAIN CLIMBING CAN BE QUITE *CALORICALLY DEMANDING*) AND DESPERATELY SEARCH *OTHER, SLEDS* FOR GOODIES. DRAWING BACK PROFESSOR JEFFRIES' TARP, SHAG AND SCOOB EXPOSE A CRATE MARKED...

DON'T TOUCH THAT -- IT'S VERY SENSITIVE EQUIPMENT!

GEEZ -- NOT THE ONLY THING *SENSITIVE* AROUND HERE, HUH SCOOB?

PEMBA, SENSING THEY ARE BEING WATCHED, SPOTS A SMALL FIGURE FOLLOWING THEM.

MINGA!

I SWEAR...I WAS HEADED IN THE *OPPOSITE DIRECTION,* BUT THEN I HEARD THE WEATHER REPORT. *A TERRIBLE SNOW STORM COMES!*

YOU AND *THAT RADIO!* EVERY DAY, ALL YOU DO IS STARE OFF INTO SPACE... LISTENING TO THAT *JABBER-MOUTHED DEE-JAY* PLAYING HIS RECORDS.

LOOK THERE!

THE EXPEDITION QUICKLY FINDS SHELTER FROM THE SNOW STORM IN A ROCKY NOOK. EXHAUSTED FROM THE TREK, EVERYONE QUICKLY SETTLES IN FOR THE NIGHT. OR SO IT SEEMS...

WRROOLL!

WHAT'S *THAT?*

RETI!

HA-HA! NOT TO WORRY, *MES AMIS!* YOU ARE SAFE WITH ME. FOR I AM *ALPHONSE LAFLEUR!* ZEE WORLD'S *GREATEST MONSTER HUNTER!* AND ONCE I CAPTURE ZEE MONSTER, THEN YOU, MESSIEURS SHAGGY AND SCOOBY, CAN GO *HOME!*

ZOINKS! LIKE, I GET IT *NOW!* THAT'S WHY WE GOT THE "*SPECIAL TOUR*"! WE'RE JUST *MONSTER BAIT* TO HELP YOU CATCH THAT *ICE COLD CRETIN!*

WHAT CAN I SAY? I READ ZEE NEWSPAPER STORY ABOUT ZEE TEENAGE "*GANG*" AND ZEE BIG DOG, *SCOOBY-DOO,* AND HOW ZEE MONSTERS, THEY CHASE THEM *EVERYWHERE* THEY GO!

MAN, LIKE, WHO SAID THERE'S NO SUCH THING AS *BAD PRESS?*

GRRRR

PLEASE, DO NOT BE *ANGRY* -- I WILL SHARE WITH YOU A LITTLE *SECRET* I HAVE LEARNED OVER ZEE YEARS.

TO *CAPTURE ZEE* MONSTER, YOU MUST *THINK* LIKE ZEE MONSTER, NO? YOU MUST WALK IN HIS *BIG MONSTER SHOES,* EH? THEN, YOU CAN DEFEAT HIM *EVERY TIME!*

≶GULP≶ LIKE, MIND IF WE TELL YOU A LITTLE SECRET, *TOO?*

WRROOLL

WELL, MAYBE *NOT* SO LITTLE...

SACRÉ BLEU!

NO -- NOT THAT WAY! YOU WILL *SPRING ALL ZEE TRAPS!!!*

ZAP

FOOLS -- I MUST *FOLLOW...*

SNAP

SNAP

SNAP

SNAP

SNAP

:GROAN:

PEMBA, ROUSED FROM SLEEP BY THE COMMOTION, ONCE AGAIN COMES FACE TO FACE WITH THE *MONSTER!* WHICH EXPLAINS WHY HE'S GAINING ON SHAGGY AND SCOOBY!

OUT OF MY WAY!

SORRY, DUDE -- EVERY MAN *AND* DOG FOR *HIMSELF!*

BUT THE GUIDE IS CAUGHT IN ANOTHER OF LAFLEUR'S TRAPS.

THE YETI LEAPS, AND SEEMS TO FLOAT DOWN.

WHILE SHAG AND SCOOB...*ROLL DOWN!*

HELLLPP

RELLLPP

WHEN THE HUMAN/DOG SNOWBALL FINALLY COMES TO A STOP, IT'S BECAUSE IT'S SMASHED INTO AN EVEN BIGGER BEAST!

RRROOAARR

YAAAAA

RAAAAA

SHAGGY? SCOOBY? IS THAT *REALLY* YOU?

DEL CHILLMAN! WHAT ARE *YOU* DOING HERE?

YO! I CAN'T BELIEVE IT'S YOU TWO! NO WAY THIS IS *COINCIDENCE*. WHAT BRINGS YOU ALL THE WAY TO *TOP OF THE WORLD?*

WOULD YOU BELIEVE WE'RE ON *VACATION?*

—RACATION!

SO, SHAGGY AND ZEE POOCHIE HAVE HITCHED A RIDE, EH? NO MATTER...

...WHERE THEY GO, *ZEE MONSTER* IS SURE TO FOLLOW!

AND, BUT OF COURSE, *ZEE MONSTER* HUNTER, HA-HA!

SORRY YOU CAN'T CALL THE REST OF THE GANG... IT LOOKS LIKE THE SNOW STORM HAS *BLOCKED OUT* THE SATELLITE.

NOW, DUDES, YOU GOTTA TELL ME EVERYTHING YOU KNOW ABOUT THE *ABOMINABLE SNOWMAN!*

ZOINKS! LIKE, WHAT'S TO KNOW? HE'S HAIRY, SCARY AND QUITE CONTRARY! WHY DO YOU CARE? LAST I HEARD, YOU WERE HUNG UP ON THE *LOCH NESS MONSTER!*

NESSIE WAS A *NO-SHOW*...I WAS SOOO BUMMED... BUT THEN IT HIT ME! WHAT IF I GOT A JOB UP HERE, AND USED MY FREE TIME TO SEARCH FOR PROOF OF *MR. ABOMINABLE?*

MT. EVEREST WEATHER STATION ELEV. 27,000 FEET NO FOOLIN'!

AT FIRST, THE YETI WAS JUST AS ELUSIVE, BUT I JUST STARTED FINDING ALL KINDS OF EVIDENCE. CHECK OUT THESE SHOTS OF GIANT, APE-LIKE FOOTPRINTS. I TOOK THIS PICTURE LAST WEEK! *AMAZINGLY RIGHTEOUS, HUH?!*

NO, MAN. WHAT'S AMAZING IS THIS *FAN MAIL.*

HA-HA. YEAH, WELL...I'M SUPPOSED TO REPORT THE WEATHER, RIGHT?

BUT I STARTED PLAYING DISCS BETWEEN THE REPORTS, AND RAPPING ABOUT THE RECORDS-- YOU KNOW, THE WHOLE DJ THING.

"DEAR DEL, THANK YOU FOR PLAYING SUCH GREAT MUSIC. I LISTEN TO YOUR SHOW EVERY DAY... I HOPE YOU NEVER LEAVE THE MOUNTAIN."

SIGNED, "YOUR NUMBER ONE FAN."

ONCE I READ THAT, DUDE, I KNEW I HAD TO JUST KEEP ON *ROCKIN'*, MAN...I ONLY WISH I COULD *STAY LONGER.*

DID I MENTION THIS COOL *YAK HAIR HAT* CAME WITH THE NOTE?

OH YEAH? WELL... UH, LIKE, IT'S REALLY... YOU.

WITH THE WEATHER IMPROVED, DEL TAKES HIS *SNOWCAT* BACK OUT TO LOOK FOR OTHER POSSIBLE STORM VICTIMS, LEAVING SHAGGY AND SCOOBY AT THE STATION TO FILL IN FOR HIM AS "GUEST DJS."

USING *YAK POWER* INSTEAD OF *HORSE POWER*, FREDDY, DAPHNE AND VELMA TRACK THEIR FRIENDS THROUGH THE HEAVY SNOW TO THE NOW-DESERTED *RANGPOCHE MONASTERY*-- SHAGGY'S LAST KNOWN POSITION!

IT'S SHAGGY AND SCOOBY, BROADCASTING LIVE FROM THE *TOP OF THE WORLD*, SPINNING STACKS OF WAX FOR ALL YOU FROSTBITTEN FANS OUT THERE.

ROOBY ROOBY ROOOOO!

YOU SURE THIS IS THE RIGHT PLACE, FREDDY?

I THINK SO...

I THINK SO *TOO* -- LOOK, *SCOOBY SNACKS*...AND *SCOOBY TRACKS*! BUT WHY WOULD THEY BE HEADING *UP* THE MOUNTAIN?!

HMMMM... DON'T KNOW, DAPH, BUT WE'VE GOT TO *STAY SHARP*! OUR NEXT CLUE WON'T BE JUST JUMPING OUT AT US FROM *THIN AIR*.

UNBEKNOWNST TO THE GANG, THEIR ANSWER WAS ON THE AIR...AND UNBEKNOWNST TO SHAGGY AND SCOOBY, THEIR MONSTER WAS ON THE *SCARE*.

MEANWHILE... THE GANG DISCOVER LARGE, APE-LIKE FOOTPRINTS...MYSTERIOUS IN *MORE WAYS THAN ONE*. FOR EVEN THOUGH THE STRANGE TRACKS ARE *THREE TIMES* THE SIZE OF DAPHNE'S DAINTY BOOTS, THE MARK THEY LEAVE IN THE SNOW IS ONLY *HALF* AS DEEP.

I HOPE EVERYONE OUT THERE ENJOYED THAT TUNE FROM *HOWLING HARRY AND THE WOLVERINES*.

SCOOBY, SHOW OUR LISTENERS THE PROPER WAY TO *HOWL*!

ROOOOOOWWLL

GUYS, TELL THE TRUTH...DO THESE MONSTER FOOTPRINTS MAKE ME LOOK *HEAVY*?

YES...HARD TO BELIEVE.

WHAT'S HARD TO BELIEVE IS THAT CREATURE IS SUCH A *LIGHTWEIGHT*!

HELP!

THERE... OPEN.

THANK YOU SO MUCH FOR *FREEING* ME. THE YETI, PLEASE BELIEVE ME, IS *NO JOKE*! IT IS HUGE AND IT IS *TERRIBLE*. ITS ARMS ARE *LONGER* THAN MY WHOLE BODY. I WATCHED IT LEAP *HIGHER* AND CLIMB *FASTER* THAN *ANY* GOAT. WE ARE ALL IN *MUCH DANGER*. I MUST OFFER PRAYERS TO THE *GREAT MOUNTAIN*. I MUST...I MUST...

FIRST, YOU MUST CALM DOWN.

BUT PEMBA CANNOT REST UNTIL HE LEARNS WHAT HAS HAPPENED TO THE OTHERS - MOST IMPORTANT, TO HIS SISTER, MINGA.

NO! THIS IS *NOT GOOD*. SHE *NEVER* GOES ANYWHERE WITHOUT THIS THING. SO, IT IS *CERTAIN*. THE CREATURE *HAS MINGA*!

AND NOW FOR ALL YOU *MOUNTAIN MUSIC LOVERS*, IT'S TIME FOR YOUR MID-MORNING *TRAFFIC REPORT*! HATE TO SAY IT, BUT THERE'S A *SIX-YAK* PILEUP ON THE TIBETAN TRI-LEVEL!

ROOBY-ROOOOO

I DON'T BELIEVE IT! LISTEN! SHAGGY AND SCOOBY!

THERE IS ONLY ONE PLACE FROM WHICH THIS COULD BE COMING... THE *WEATHER STATION*.

CONTINUED ON PAGE 51

Tick as you find...

20 ghosts ✓

6 spiders ✓

10 bats ✓

4 pairs of evil eyes ✓

8 rats ✓

2 black cats ✓

Bonus Items!

A ghost with a top hat

Scooby hiding ✓

Anti-spook potion

Eye Spy!

Tick each time you spot a change!

BITESIZE FACTS!

BACK IN THE 18TH CENTURY, POWDERED EGYPTIAN MUMMIES WERE USED AS MEDICINE. IT WORKS ESPECIALLY WELL IF YOU'VE BEEN COFFIN A LOT LATELY!

WORRIED ABOUT A SPOOK VISITING YOUR HOUSE? PUT ROSEMARY (THAT'S THE HERB, NOT THE GIRL IN YOUR CLASS) BY THE DOOR AND IT WILL SCARE ANY GHOULISH SPIRITS AWAY. PUTTING A HORSESHOE ON YOUR DOOR WILL ALSO DO THE TRICK.

LEGEND HAS IT THAT IF TWO PEOPLE WANDER AROUND IN A DARK ROOM AT MIDNIGHT ON 2ND NOVEMBER, THEY WILL NEVER SEE EACH OTHER AGAIN! SPOOKY!

VAMPIRE BATS DO NOT DRINK HUMAN BLOOD. HOWEVER, THEY DO FEED ON THE BLOOD OF CATTLE, LARGE BIRDS, HORSES AND PIGS.

THE DRACULA WE KNOW TODAY IS FROM BRAM STOKER'S NOVEL "DRACULA" WRITTEN IN 1897. BRAM STOKER BASED HIS TALE ON A REAL-LIFE HISTORICAL CHARACTER KNOWN AS VLAD THE IMPALER. VLAD WASN'T A VAMPIRE BUT HE WAS A BLOODTHIRSTY WRETCH, FAMOUS FOR PUNISHING HIS ENEMIES IN GRUESOME WAYS!

THE WORD 'GHOUL' IS USED AS A GENERAL WORD FOR GHOSTS, BUT IT ORIGINATED IN THE MIDDLE EAST AS A NAME FOR AN EVIL SPIRIT WHO FEEDS ON HUMAN FLESH. AS YOU CAN IMAGINE, THEY DIDN'T HAVE MANY FRIENDS AND LIVED IN LONELY PLACES LIKE THE DESERT.

ACCORDING TO FOLKLORE, YOU SHOULD TIE BROOMS DOWN ON 6TH JANUARY TO STOP THEM BEING USED BY WITCHES!

IT WAS BELIEVED THAT SOULS COULD TRAVEL BACK TO THE WORLD OF THE LIVING IN THE BODY OF AN ANIMAL, USUALLY A BLACK CAT.

SALT IS HANDY FOR SCARING SPOOKS AWAY, AND IT BRINGS YOU GOOD LUCK. THROW A PINCH OVER YOUR LEFT SHOULDER. IT WILL HIT THE SPOOK IN THE EYE AND BLIND IT!

GRRAARR

≈GULP≈ HE *COULD* THINK LIKE A *MONSTER,* SCOOB -- JUST NOT AS FAST!

BUT, MAN, *HE'S LUCKIER THAN US* ...BECAUSE, LIKE...WE'VE STILL GOT A *YETI* ON OUR TAILS!

SCOOBY'S PAW BRUSHES AGAINST A VALVE THAT INSTANTLY INFLATES A WEATHER BALLOON. AND JUST IN THE NICK OF TIME, THEY FLOAT FROM THE CREATURE'S GRASP!

MERE MOMENTS LATER, FRED AND VELMA ARRIVE AT THE WEATHER STATION, SURPRISED TO FIND THEIR OLD FRIEND DEL. BUT DEL'S EVEN MORE SURPRISED TO DISCOVER THAT THE WEATHER STATION HAS BEEN DESTROYED...AND SHAGGY AND SCOOBY ARE GONE!

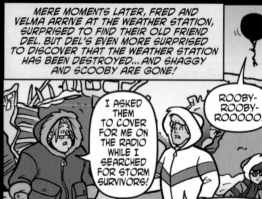

I ASKED THEM TO COVER FOR ME ON THE RADIO WHILE I SEARCHED FOR STORM SURVIVORS!

ROOBY- ROOBY- ROOOOO!

MEANWHILE, IT LOOKS LIKE THEY, AND THE WEATHER STATION, HAD MORE *MONSTER* THAN THEY COULD HANDLE.

COSMICALLY IRONIC, *HUH?*

TEN MINUTES INTO THE GANG'S INVESTIGATION...

HOLD ON. MAYBE THERE WAS SOMETHING ELSE HERE THAT THE SNOWMAN WAS AFTER, *BESIDES* SHAGGY AND SCOOBY.

HELIUM TANKS?

YEAH, WE USE 'EM TO FILL UP THE WEATHER BALLOONS ...BUT THERE ARE SOME MISSING.

WHAT WOULD A SNOW CREATURE WANT WITH *PRESSURIZED HELIUM?*

WHOA! CHECK OUT THIS SEISMOGRAPH. IT DETECTS UNDERGROUND VIBRATIONS, AND IT'S PICKING UP SOME REALLY STRANGE ONES DEEP INSIDE THE MOUNTAIN.

THE LINES SPIKE LIKE A SERIES OF SMALL EARTHQUAKES.

CHCH CHCH CHCH

OR, MAYBE... *EXPLOSIONS!* BUT WHAT'S THE CONNECTION BETWEEN THE MISSING HELIUM TANKS AND UNDERGROUND BLASTS?

I DON'T KNOW, VELMA, BUT I'LL BET THE ANSWER *BLOWS* THE LID OFF *THIS* MYSTERY!

DAPHNE AND PEMBA REACH THE YETI'S CAVE AND DISCOVER IT LEADS STRAIGHT *DOWN* INTO THE MOUNTAIN.

OH MAN... WE'RE *GOING DOWN!*

WELL, PEMBA, I GUESS YOU'RE RIGHT... IF I WERE AN *ABOMINABLE SNOWMAN*, THIS WOULD BE *MY* LAIR.

AS THEIR DEFLATING BALLOON SLOWLY DESCENDS, SHAGGY AND SCOOBY CROSS OVER INTO AN ANCIENT *LOST CITY*, BOTH BEAUTIFUL *AND... TROPICAL!*

ZOINKS! LIKE, WHAT KIND OF PLACE *IS* THIS?

HUH?

FEAR NOT, HONORED ONES. YOUR GOOD KARMA HAS AT LAST BROUGHT YOU TO A PLACE OF *PEACE...*

HOLY SMOKE, SCOOB! LIKE, GET A LOAD OF THIS PLACE!

WELCOME, MY FRIENDS, TO THE LOST KINGDOM OF SHANGRI-LA. FOR CENTURIES, THIS WAS THE VERY HEART OF THE HIMALAYAS. AN EARTHLY PARADISE, WHERE SEEKERS OF TRUTH SOUGHT REFUGE FROM THE OUTSIDE WORLD.

UH... PARDON ME, YOUR HIGH *LAMA-NESS*. BUT LIKE, WHAT HAPPENED TO THIS PLACE?

MANY YEARS AGO, MEN CAME FROM THE OUTSIDE WORLD, DRIVEN BY ANGER AND GREED. PARADISE WAS *LOST*.

HEY, WONDER IF THAT'S WHY THE ABOMINABLE SNOWMAN HAS SUCH A *CHILLY* PERSONALITY! LIKE, MAYBE HE'S JUST BEEN TRYING TO PROTECT THIS PLACE FROM THE *OUTSIDE WORLD!*

VERY *WISE*, HONORED ONE. I WILL SHOW YOU TO YOUR CHAMBERS WITHIN. STAY AS LONG AS YOU WISH.

KA-BOOM

RUMBLE

HUH?!

WHAT?!

A DEEP CHASM OPENS IN THE WALL OF THE CAVE.

JEEPERS! WHAT WAS THAT?

I THINK THE ANSWER LIES DOWN THERE!

SHAGGY AND SCOOBY SEARCH THE DARKENED HALLWAYS OF SHANGRI-LA FOR A BATHROOM. INSTEAD, THEY STUMBLE UPON A DECAYING SECTION OF THE CITY, COVERED WITH MURALS OF DEMONS!

GEE, FOR SUCH A PEACEFUL PEOPLE, THEY SURE HAD A LOT OF CREEPY PAINTINGS!

REAH... REEPY.

GUESS IT'S ALL PART OF THEIR RELIGION. LIKE, CHECK THIS GUY OUT, SCOOB! HE MUST BE THE GOD OF BAD BREATH!

REE-HEE-HEE!

≤SNIFF≥ ≤SNIFF≥ HEY, HE REALLY DOES HAVE BAD BREATH!

AND BAD BREATH MEANS....

RRRAARR

REATHING!

OH, MAN -- THESE MURALS ARE TOO REALISTIC!

AFTER GIVING THE SNOWMAN THE SLIP –
BY ACCIDENTALLY *SLIPPING* DOWN A CREVASSE IN THE
WALL – SHAGGY AND SCOOBY TUMBLE DOWN A TUNNEL
THAT LEADS THEM TO THEIR FRIENDS...DEEP IN
THE *HEART* OF THE MOUNTAIN!

WHAT A
WILD RIDE! BUT --
DEL...THE GANG...ALL
HERE -- THAT'S EVEN
WILDER!

REAH – RILD!

SHAGGY!
SCOOBY!

SHAGGY!
SCOOBY!

NO TIME FOR PROPER
GREETINGS. WE ARE IN
GREAT DANGER! THIS
CAVE COULD COLLAPSE
AT ANY MOMENT!

RUMBLE

KA-BOOM!

THEY RUN INTO ANOTHER TUNNEL, WHICH LEADS TO A
LEDGE, OVERLOOKING A VAST CAVERN, FILLED WITH
SHIMMERING CRYSTALS. EVERYONE STOPS TO STARE.

WOW!

NOW,
THAT'S AN
UNDERGROUND
SCENE I CAN
DIG!

≥GASP≤
SOMEONE'S
DOWN THERE!

USING THE BINOCULARS, FREDDY
FOLLOWS THE FIGURE'S
ACTIONS FROM AFAR.

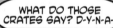

LOOKS LIKE HE'S
PACKED SOMETHING
LIKE...*STICKS*...BEHIND A
HUGE CHUNK OF CRYSTAL...
HE'S DUCKING BEHIND THAT
PILE OF *ROCKS*...WITH
SOME KIND OF *DEVICE*
IN HIS HANDS.

WHAT DO THOSE
CRATES SAY? D-Y-N-A–

DYNAMITE!

IT'S *PROFESSOR JEFFRIES!* I SHOULD
HAVE KNOWN! SO, HE IS BLOWING UP THE
CAVERN TO STEAL THE *SACRED*
CRYSTALS!

JEEPERS!

KA-BOOM

COME ON, GANG,
WE'VE GOT TO GET DOWN THERE
FAST! I'VE GOT A PLAN TO CATCH
THIS *CRYSTAL CRAVING CREEP!*

AFTER GATHERING HIS MINING EQUIPMENT, THE GLOATING PROFESSOR TURNS TO CHECK ON HIS *ILL-GOTTEN GAINS*, AND DISCOVERS...

WHAT...WHERE'S THE *CRYSTAL* I JUST PUT ON THE... HEY, WHERE'S THE *SLED*?!

ROO-HOO!

LOOKING FOR SOMETHING, MAN?

WHY *YOU...!* THAT'S *MY PRICELESS* CRYSTAL!

JUST AS FREDDY PLANNED, PROFESSOR JEFFRIES GIVES CHASE...FOLLOWING SHAGGY AND SCOOBY RIGHT INTO THE TRAP THE GANG CREATED FROM THEIR CLIMBING EQUIPMENT.

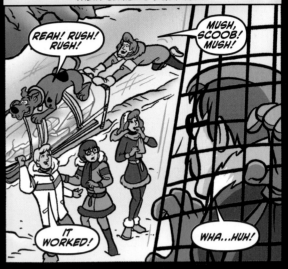

REAH! RUSH! RUSH!

MUSH, SCOOB! MUSH!

IT WORKED!

WHA...HUH!

PROFESSOR JEFFRIES, WE PRESUME?

NOW THAT'S A *TEXTBOOK* EXAMPLE OF HOW TO CATCH A *WANNABE SNOW MONSTER.*

SORRY, PROFESSOR, BUT IT MAKES *PERFECT SENSE.* YOU'VE BEEN USING *THE LEGEND* TO SCARE EVERYONE OFF THE MOUNTAIN...

NO, NO -- YOU'VE GOT IT *ALL* WRONG! *I'M NOT THE SNOWMAN!*

RRRNNN

LIKE, *MUSH!*

THE QUICKEST ESCAPE IS BY SLED, BUT THE MONSTER GRABS ONE TOO! AND NOT JUST ANY SLED! THE ONE WITH THE *DYNAMITE!* WHAT FOLLOWS IS A CRAZY SLED CHASE THROUGH THE MOUNTAIN (WHICH WE ARE ABLE TO SEE THANKS TO THIS NIFTY *CUT-AWAY VIEW*).

WOOSH

EVEN PROFESSOR JEFFRIES GETS IN ON THE *UNDERGROUND CHASE*, AFTER USING HIS TRUSTY *SWISS ARMY KNIFE* (REMEMBER HOW OUR STORY BEGAN?) TO CUT THROUGH THE MAKESHIFT TRAP!

THE SLEDS SLIP AND SLIDE THROUGH THE TUNNELS LIKE BUMPER CARS, UNTIL THEY ALL CRASH, BOUNCING THE RIDERS INTO THE AIR! THE YETI LANDS IN SHAG AND SCOOB'S SLED, WHILE THEY WIND UP IN ...≑GULP≑... THE ONE FULL OF EXPLOSIVES!

IN THE DARKNESS, SCOOBY LIGHTS A "CANDLE" HE FINDS IN ONE OF THE BOXES. CURIOUSLY, THE WORD WRITTEN ON THE CRATES IS THE SAME AS ON HIS "CANDLE." DYNAMITE!

BOOOM BOOOM

WHICH EXPLAINS - FINALLY! - THE HUGE EXPLOSION BLASTING EVERYONE OUT OF THE MOUNTAIN! AND THEN...OH...IT'S *TOO MUCH!* NO MORE *CAPTIONS!*

WOW -- WE MADE IT... I THINK.

≋GROAN≋ NO BROKEN BONES...?

WHAT...?

JUST FROZEN BUTT!

...IS THIS?!

WUMP

JUST ONE OF THE *MANY* CRYSTALS FROM INSIDE THE MOUNTAIN THAT THE GOOD PROFESSOR HERE WAS TRYING TO *RIP OFF*.

EXTRAORDINARY. AND NOW *YOU* HAVE CAPTURED HIM.

WELL, ME AND THE GANG, AND... HEY, SPEAKING OF WHICH -- *WHERE'S SHAGGY AND SCOOB?!*

AH, I BELIEVE THAT IS THEM, IS IT NOT? UP THERE, RIDING ON TOP OF AN *AVALANCHE*.

I'M BACK! WOW! AND WHAT A *CAPTION* THIS IS! *HOLY LAMA!* THE FORCE OF THE ENTIRE CRATE OF DYNAMITE EXPLODING AT ONCE CREATES A MASSIVE *AVALANCHE!*

WAY TO GO, SCOOB! LIKE, LET'S *SHRED* THIS MOUNTAIN BEFORE IT SHREDS *US!*

SCOOBY-DOOBY-DOOOOO!

BUT BEFORE THE WAVE OF SNOW CAN CRUSH SHAGGY AND SCOOBY, THE CANNY CANINE CREATES TWO QUASI-SNOWBOARDS CRAFTED FROM THE DEBRIS OF THE DYNAMITED SLED. TOGETHER, MAN AND MUTT *RIDE* THE AVALANCHE DOWN TO SAFETY...*KARMA* WILLING.

FREDDY - *HEADS UP!* I'VE LOGGED ENOUGH HOURS ON THE BOARD TO KNOW THEY ARE *NOT* HEADED FOR A SWEET LANDING... UNLESS WE MAKE A PATH THEY CAN FOLLOW.

DEL? THE SNOWCAT!

THAT'S RIGHT, MAN! I NEED YOU TO GUIDE ME, USING THIS TWO-WAY RADIO, FRED!

BUT DEL -

NO TIME TO DEBATE! NOW YOU GUYS GET OVER WHERE IT'S *SAFE!*

RRRRRR

HUH?!

THE YETI!?

INSTEAD OF ATTACKING THE GANG, THE CREATURE RUNS TOWARD DEL, SHAGGY, SCOOBY... AND THE AVALANCHE!

OH, MAN -- NEVER GONNA GET OUT OF THE WAY IN TIME!

BUT THE CREATURE LEAPS MIGHTILY OVER THE SNOWCAT AND SAVES DEL, SHAG AND SCOOB, MAGICALLY FLOATING THEM ABOVE THE *WHITE FLAKES OF CARNAGE!*

FINALLY THE AVALANCHE SUBSIDES... AT THE GRAND STAIRWAY ENTRANCE OF SHANGRI-LA.

A FLYING ABOMINABLE SNOWMAN? MY MIND IS BLOWN!

NOT A FLYING SNOW-MAN, DEL!

TRY *SNOW-WOMAN!* IT WAS MINGA BEHIND THIS MONSTER MYSTERY FROM THE BEGINNING. SHE USED HELIUM TANKS FROM THE WEATHER STATION TO FILL HER LIGHTER-THAN-AIR MONSTER COSTUME.

THAT'S HOW THE YETI WAS ABLE TO CLIMB SO EASILY... AND WHY THE MONSTER'S FOOTPRINTS DIDN'T SINK VERY DEEPLY INTO THE SNOW.

I'M VERY SORRY. I NEVER MEANT TO HURT ANYONE... ESPECIALLY MY BROTHER, PEMBA.

ALL I REALLY WANTED WAS TO LISTEN TO DEL CHILLMAN ON THE RADIO... YOU SEE, I AM YOUR NUMBER ONE FAN.

WHA... HUH?

WHEN YOU ANNOUNCED ON YOUR SHOW THAT YOU WERE GOING TO BE LEAVING THE MOUNTAIN, I BROUGHT THE YETI TO LIFE AS A WAY OF KEEPING YOU *HERE.*

I GET IT... THAT'S WHY SHE WAS TRYING SO HARD TO SCARE US. SHE JUST WANTED TO CONVINCE DEL TO STICK AROUND.

WOW! REALLY! THAT'S SOOOO...

WAIT, LET ME US MY RADIO VOICE...I MEAN, *THAT'S REAALLY COOOL, MAMA.*

OOOOH!

AS FOR PROFESSOR JEFFRIES, HE WAS ONLY USING THE LEGEND OF THE YETI TO COVER UP HIS SCHEME.

AND I WOULD HAVE GOTTEN AWAY WITH IT TOO, IF IT WEREN'T FOR YOU *MEDDLING KIDS,* AND THAT MOUNTAIN CLIMBING MUTT, *SCOOBY-DOO!*

SO LIKE, IS THE ABOMINABLE SNOWMAN REALLY JUST A MYTH AFTER ALL?

NO, MES AMIS!

ZEE ABOMINABLE SNOWMAN IS REAL!!!

LAFLEUR REMEMBERS...

AFTER ZEE FLIP FROM ZEE RADIO TOWER, I SLIPPED DOWN AN EMBANK-MENT. I WAS NEARLY FALLING OFF ZEE MOUNTAIN, CLUTCHING A LITTLE LEDGE OF ICE! TEN ZOUSAND FEET BELOW ME LAY CERTAIN DEATH! I WOULD MOST CERTAINLY HAVE FALLEN, HAD NOT SOME...THING...SAVED ME!

ZEE SHOCK...I BLACKED OUT. ZEE NEXT THING I KNOW I AM SAFE ON ZEE MOUNTAIN, ALL ALONE. I REMEMBER NOTHING ELSE...

ZOINKS! LIKE, I THINK YOU'VE REMEMBERED PLENTY!

AT LAST, I HAVE MET ZEE MONSTER. BUT...IN TRUTH, I DISCOVER, IT IS NO MONSTER. INSTEAD, ZEE MONSTER HUNTER FOUND...A FRIEND!

THE LEGEND OF THE YETI LIVES ON...AS TIMELESS AS THE HEART OF THE MOUNTAIN ITSELF!

I'M REALLY SORRY FOR ALL THE TROUBLE I CAUSED...

GEE, MINGA. WHAT YOU DID IS SO, YOU KNOW...ROMANTIC... IN A KIND OF TWISTED WAY... WHICH I LIKE! I'M JUST NOT SURE WHERE WE GO FROM HERE...

I'VE GOT AN IDEA.

AH, MA CHERIE AMOR! MA PETITE BAGUETTE, NON?

HA-HA! YOUR "FRENCH" RADIO VOICE SOUNDS EVEN BETTER! OH, I AM LOVING PARIS!

THEY SAY PARIS IS FOR LOVERS, RIGHT, SCOOB? WELL, I'M IN LOVE WITH THIS SPRINGTIME SPREAD!

RE ROO!

ANSWERS!

GROOVY GAMES!

FREAK I.D.!

A) Mystery Stink. B) 203373.
C) SD logo reversed.
D) The gang missing from the Mystery Machine. E) 'C' is missing

Fake I.D.s

A) Member of Mystery Stink. 20373
B) Member of Mystery Inc. 203373
C) Member of Mystery Inc. 20370
D) Member of Mystery Inc. 20373
E) Member of Mystery Inc. 20373

PHOTO FIX!

piece that doesn't belong?

SCOOBY WHO?

ANSWER: Fred and Velma

RACE AGAINST TIME!

Start

Finish

SCUBA-DOO!

Start

Finish

SPOOK SPOTTER!

Mystery Inc. are investigating a seriously haunted house, and they need YOUR help to spot all the spooks! Can you find them all?

Tick as you find...
- 20 ghosts
- 10 bats
- 8 rats
- 6 spiders
- 4 pairs of evil eyes
- 2 black cats

Bonus Items!
- A ghost with a top hat
- Scooby hiding
- Anti-spook potion

Eye Spy!